THE

CRAWLY CRAWLY CATERPILLAR

H. E. TODD

ILLUSTRATED BY VAL BIRO

CAROUSEL

It all started with an egg.

It wasn't a hen's brown egg,

nor a duck's green egg,

nor even a blackbird's
spotted egg.

And it was nothing like a
crocodile's large white egg.

It was a tiny grey blob,
lying on a nettle leaf,
like this :–

Then that little egg turned a darker grey and something broke out of it.

It wasn't a chick,

nor a duckling,

nor a baby blackbird.

And it certainly was not a baby crocodile!

It was a little crawly thing like this:–

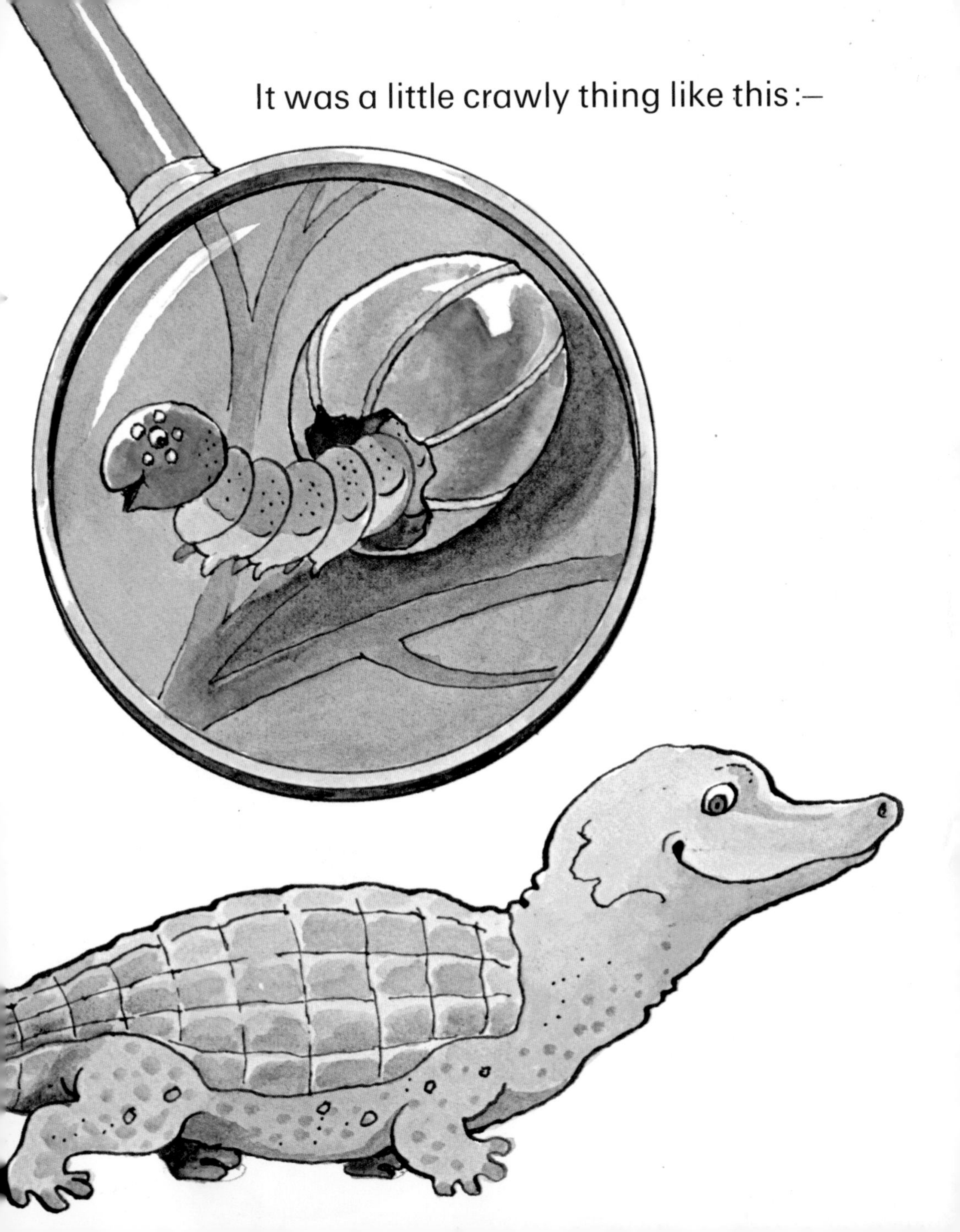

Whatever would it grow into?

Not a creepy spider,

nor a squiggly earwig,

nor a wriggly
worm,

and not even a
slithery snake –

but a

a bristly crawly caterpillar

with a yellow tummy, like this:–

He had a head and his body was built
into thirteen parts.

One at the front behind his head,
one for each letter of his name,
and one at the tail to help him
to hang onto things.

And he had –

not two eyes,
nor four eyes,
nor even eight eyes
but, believe it or not,
he had twelve tiny eyes
(six on each side of
his head).

AND

not two legs,
or even four legs,
but three pairs of
legs near the front,
and,
four pairs of hooked
legs further back
(making fourteen
legs altogether).

And he looked like this:–

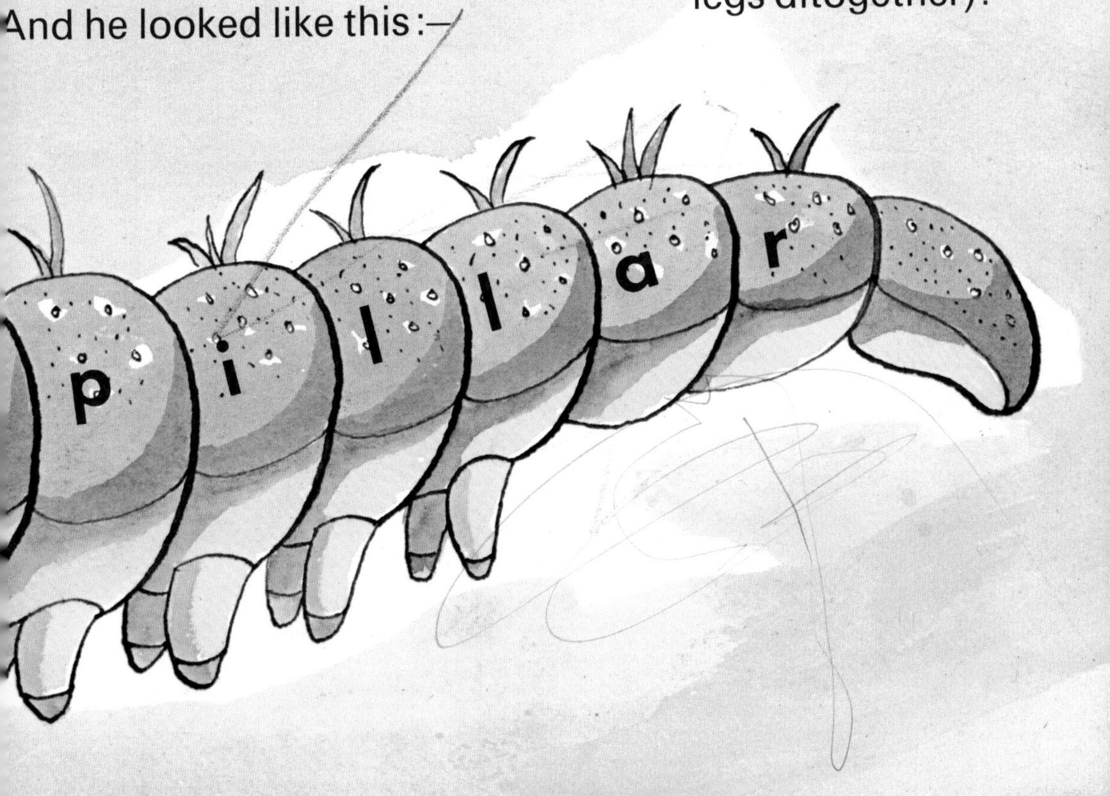

At first it was difficult to crawl
because his

and then his

and then there was trouble with his

But when he could
use all his fourteen
legs together,
he crawled along

and along and up and up and up and up a stem and over

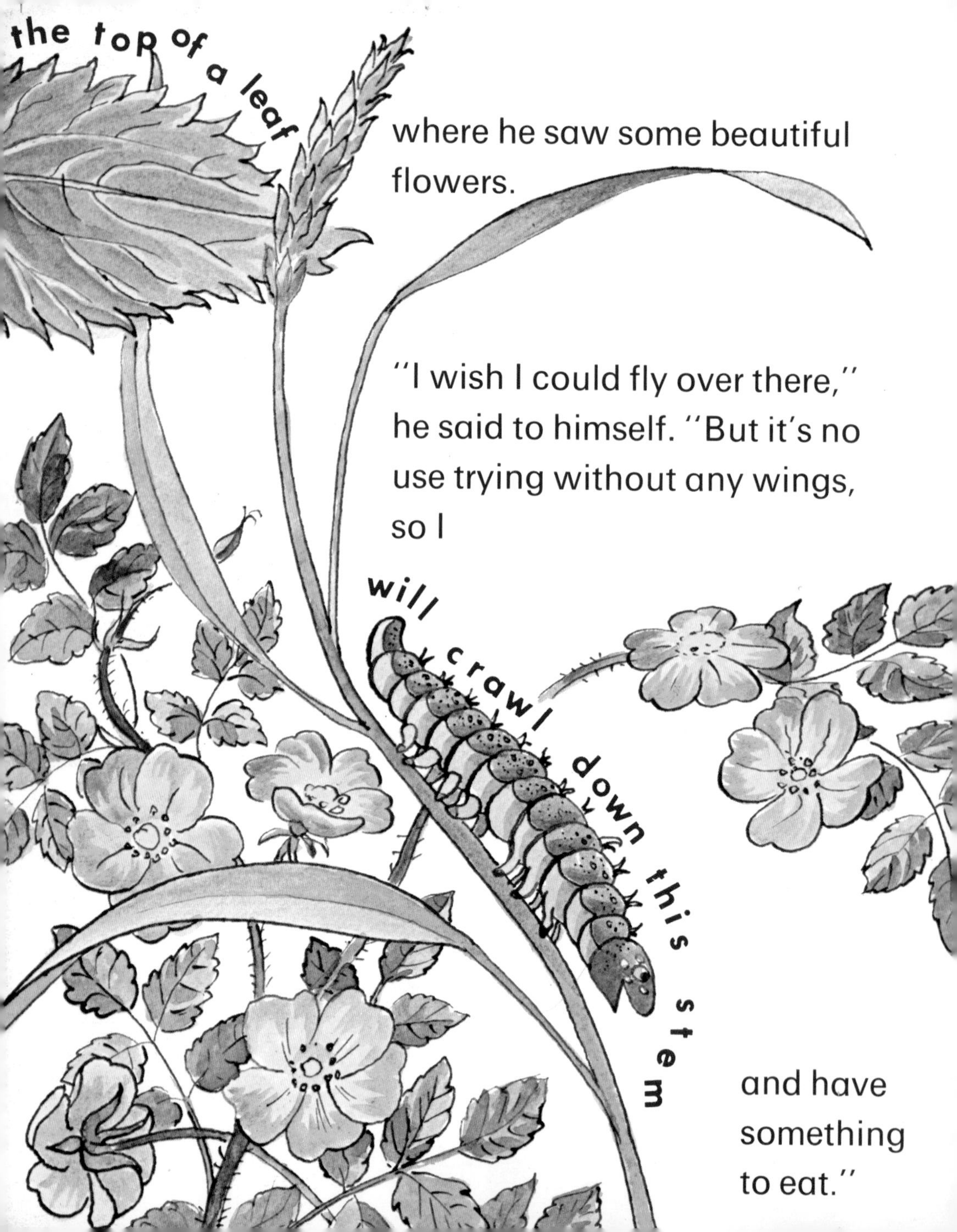

the top of a leaf where he saw some beautiful flowers.

"I wish I could fly over there," he said to himself. "But it's no use trying without any wings, so I will crawl down this stem and have something to eat."

What do you think he ate?

Not a lettuce leaf
(which slugs sometimes eat);

nor a juicy pear
(which wasps sometimes eat);

nor a rosy apple
(which worms sometimes eat);

and of course not fish fingers
(which you sometimes eat);

but

STINGING NETTLES!

He did not chew with

his mouth up and down

He chewed from side to side

first he chewed down one edge of

ettle then underneath, then up the other edge and onto the nex

page.

"I *do* wish I could fly," he said to himself again. "But I still have no wings so I suppose I shall just have to go on eating stinging nettles."

And he ate and

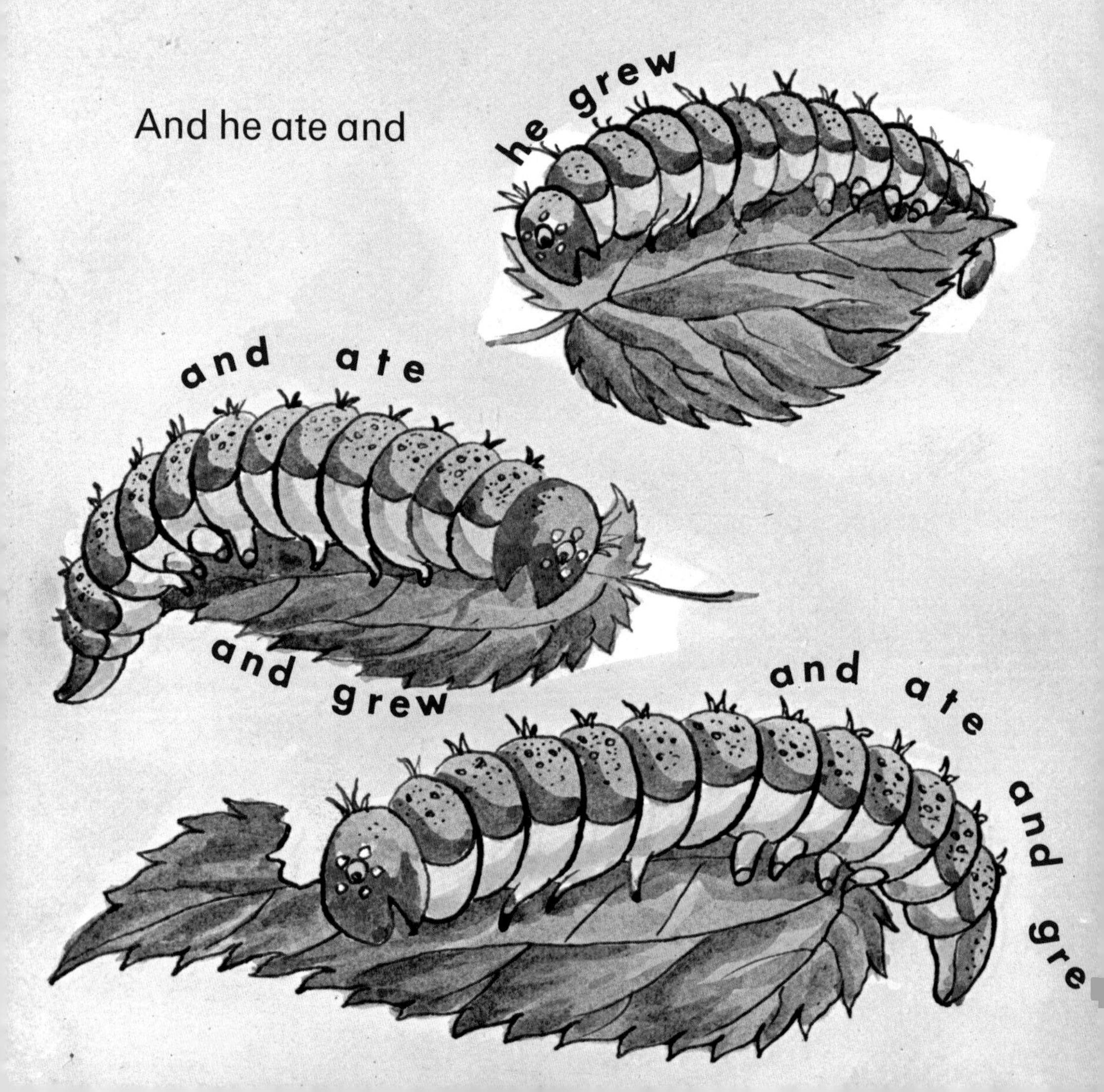

until the skin on the back of his neck burst. Then he

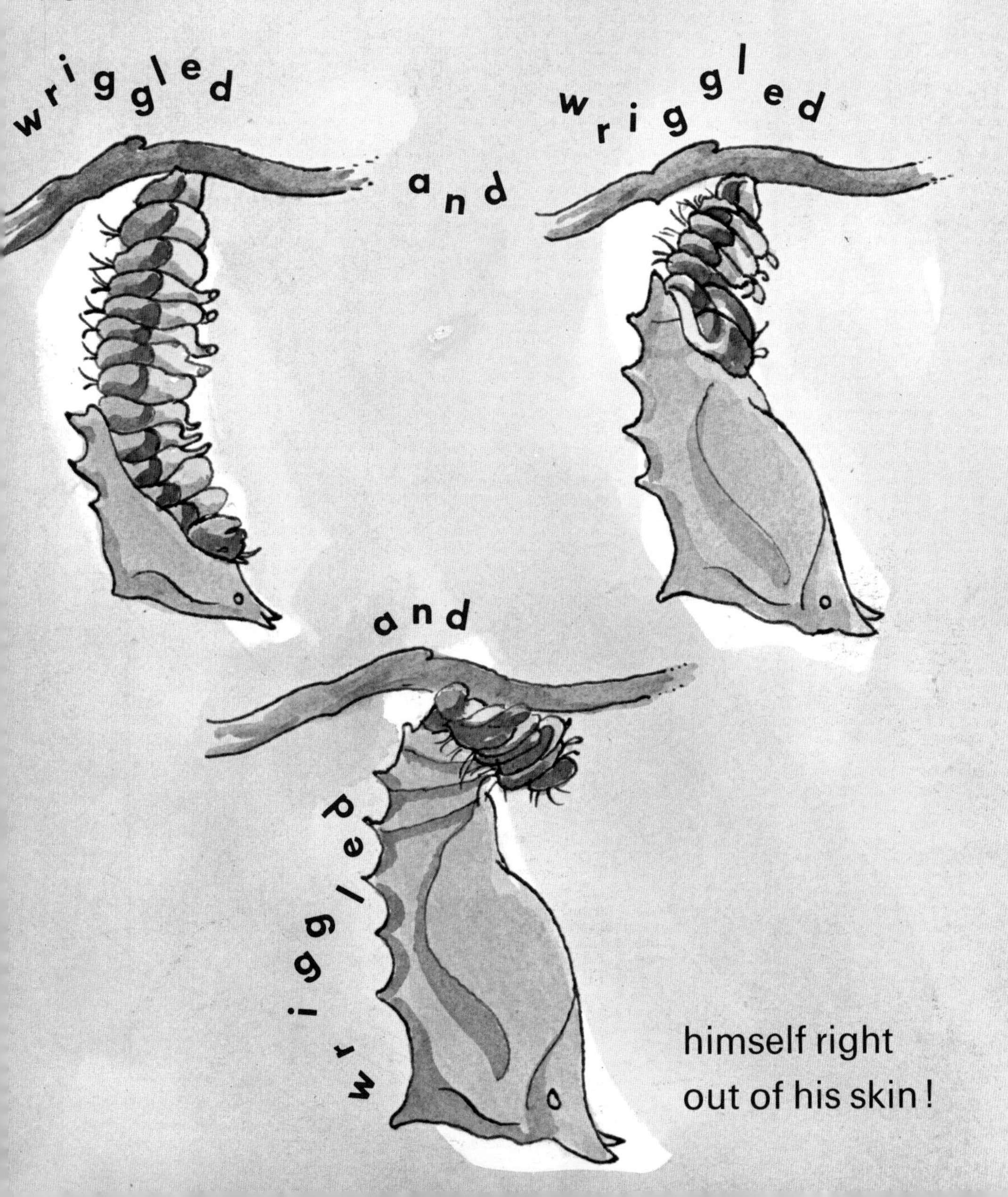

himself right out of his skin!

Then he was a funny looking thing with
a soft pupa skin.
He did not have two legs,
nor four legs,
nor even fourteen legs,
but no legs at all!
And he didn't even have a mouth!
He was no longer a caterpillar,
but had turned into something
called a chrysalis, like this:–

He could not crawl, and he could not eat, so he went to sleep and dreamed about being able to fly. While he was dreaming, wonderful things were happening inside his chrysalis. After a few days it started to

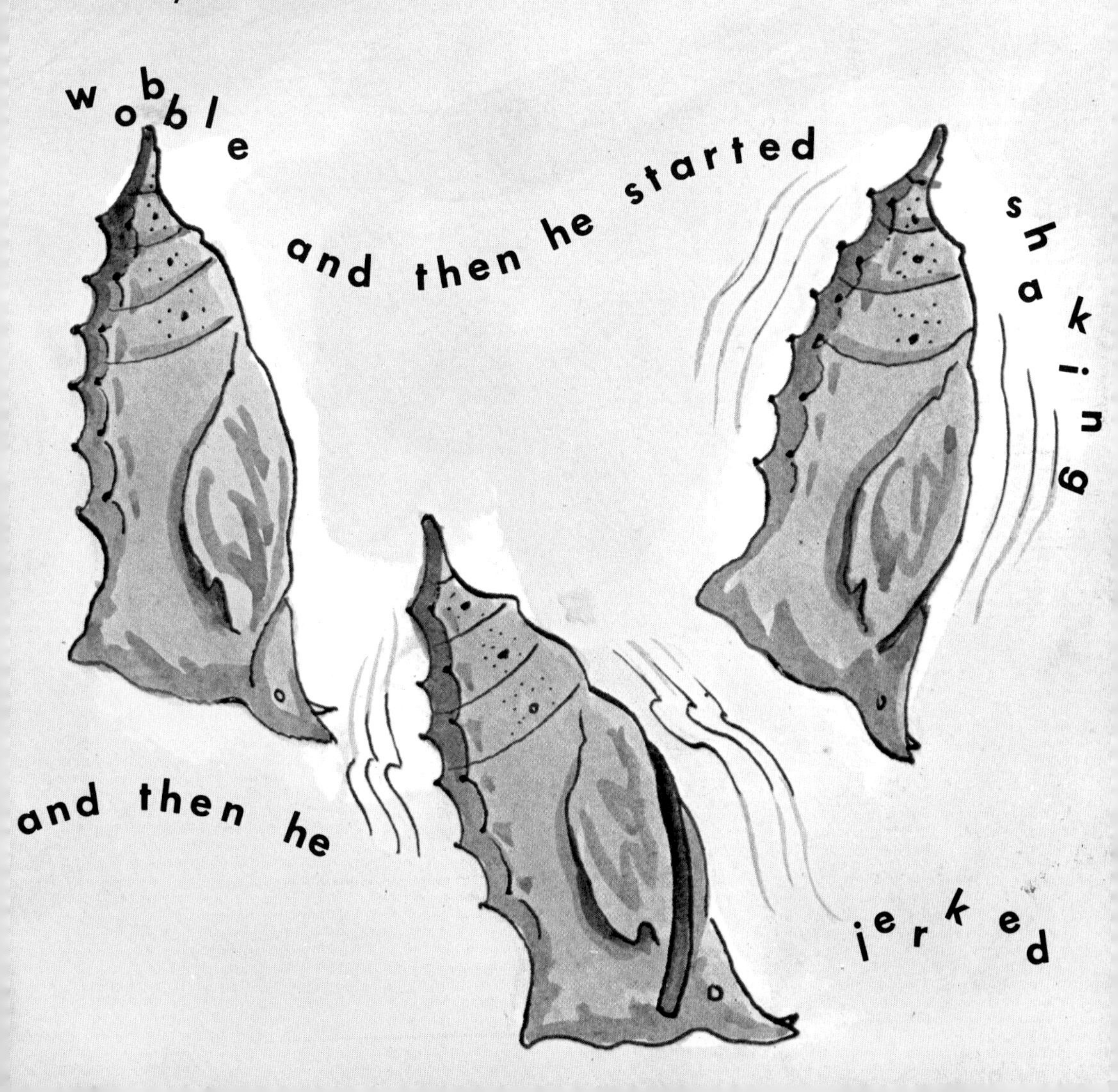

and with one last sudden 

out popped a head

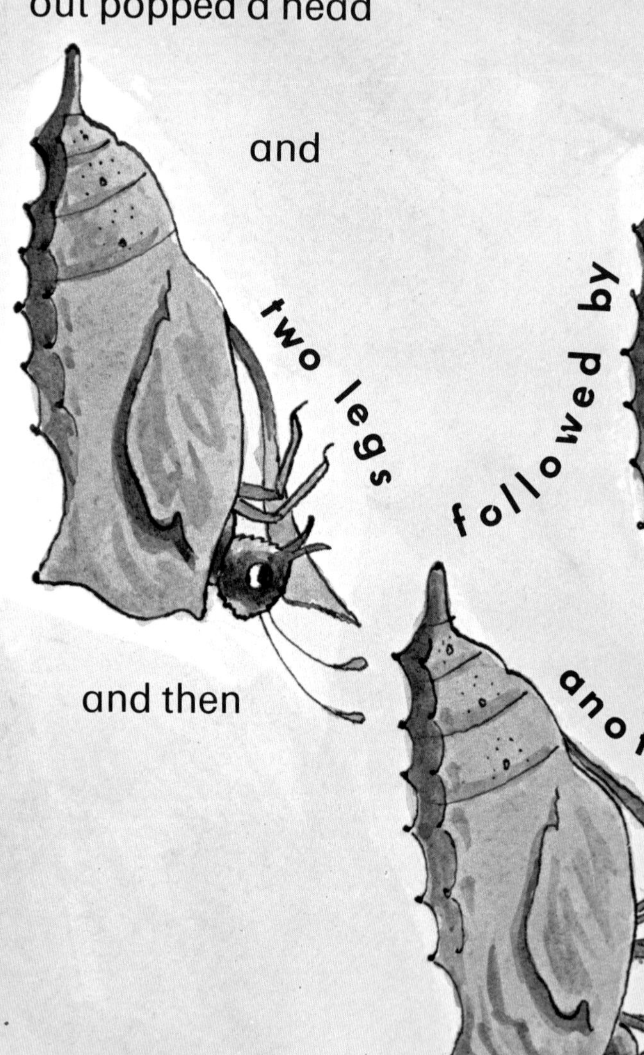

and

two legs

and then

followed by

two more legs

another pair of legs

(making six legs in all).

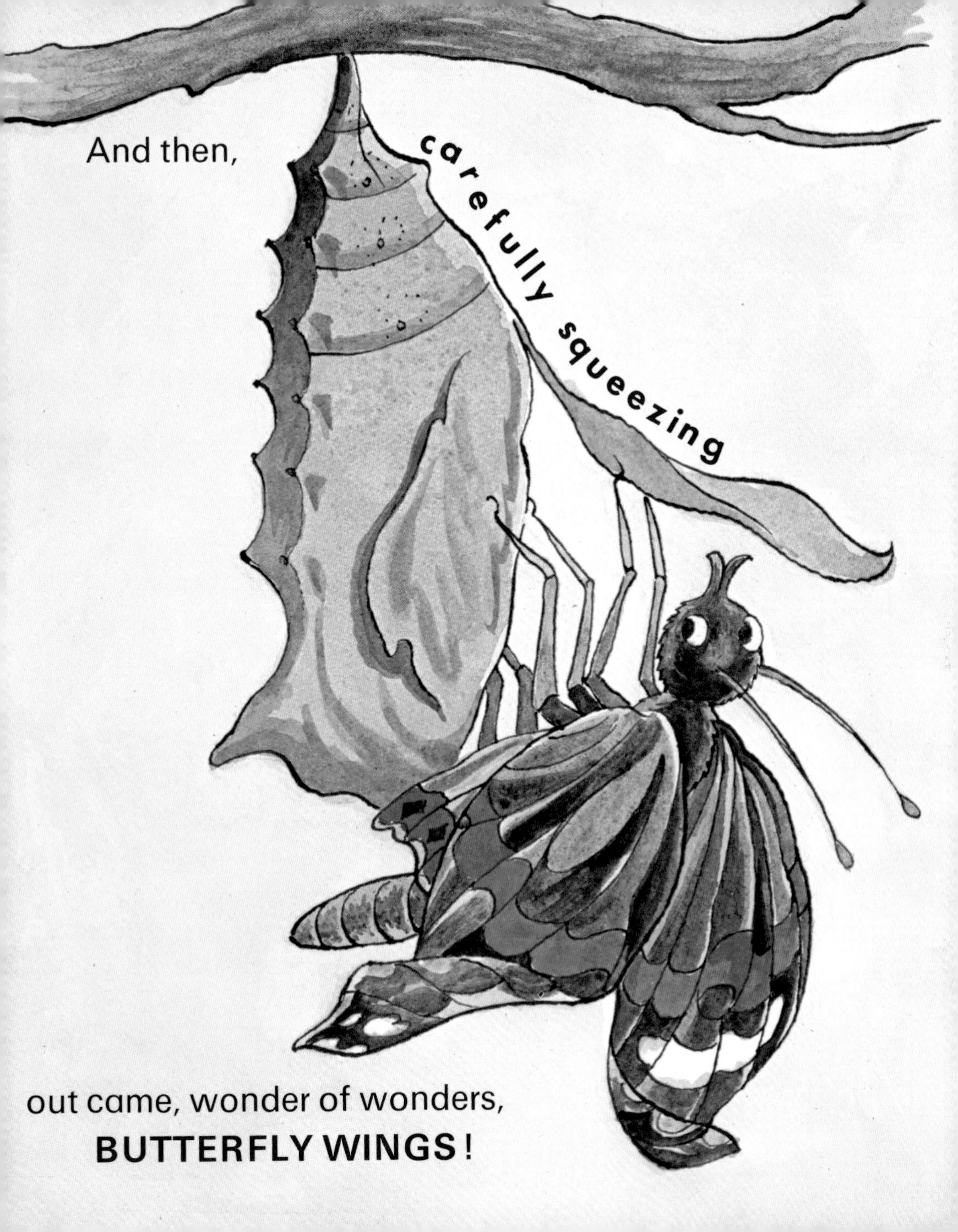
And then,
carefully squeezing
out came, wonder of wonders,
BUTTERFLY WINGS!

At first he stood trembling with his closed wings crumpled and damp.

"I wonder what sort of butterfly I am?" he asked himself.

"Am I a Cabbage White?

Or am I a Yellow Brimstone?

Am I a Spotted Tortoiseshell?

Or perhaps I am a
proud Purple Peacock?"

When he felt strong enough to
open his wings, there he stood,

the most handsome Red Admiral you ever saw, with red, black and white glossy wings shimmering in the sun.

"Now I really can fly," he cried,

nd he flew up and up and up and up right off this page and away

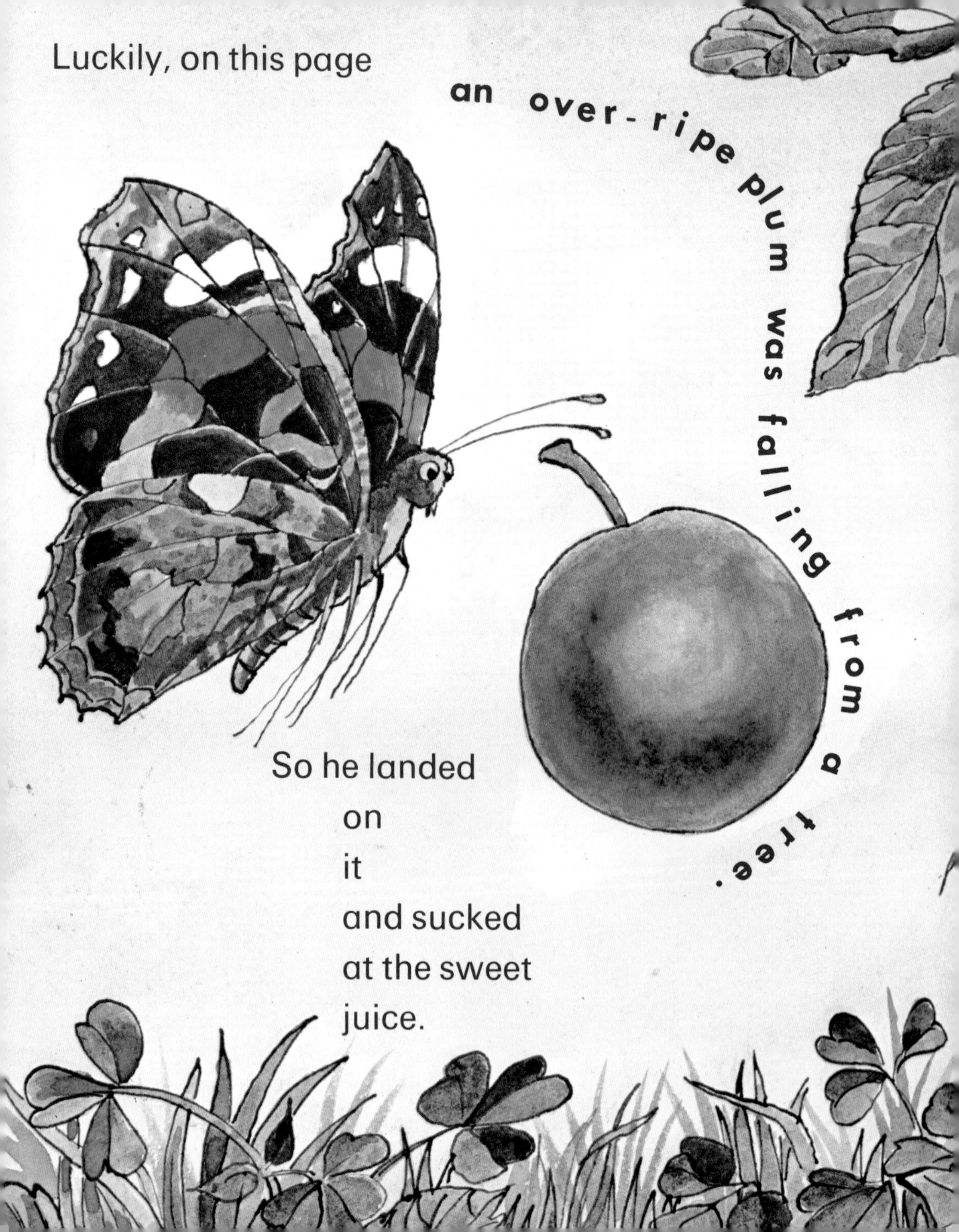
Luckily, on this page
an over-ripe plum was falling from a tree.
So he landed
on
it
and sucked
at the sweet
juice.

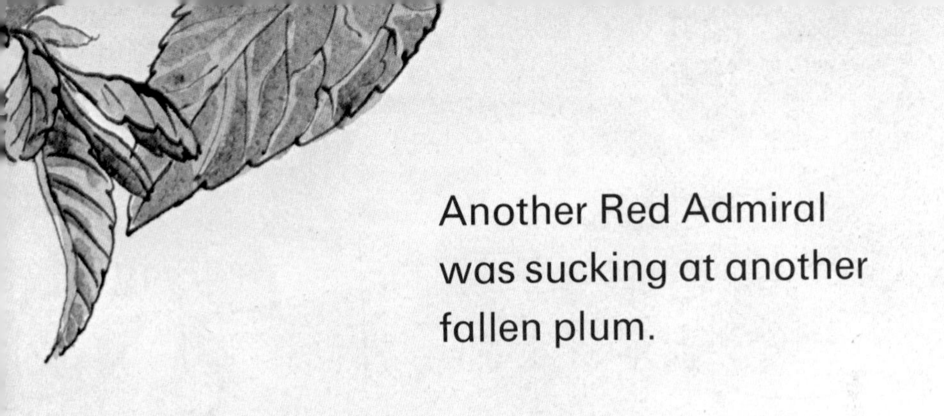

Another Red Admiral
was sucking at another
fallen plum.

She was the most
beautiful butterfly
he had ever seen.

He flew over to her,
and flapped his wings
at her, just to show
off.

then they flew round the plum tree together.

Throughout the next day they flew among the hills together.

It would take too many pages to show all the lovely places they found, but here is one of them :–

They had a lovely day and then they flew higher and higher and up and away together.

And then the Red Admiral's Lady flew down and she

laid a tiny grey egg on a nettle leaf, like this:–

Soon that little egg turned a darker grey and something broke out of it. It was a little crawly thing which grew into a bristly crawly caterpillar with a yellow tummy, like this:–

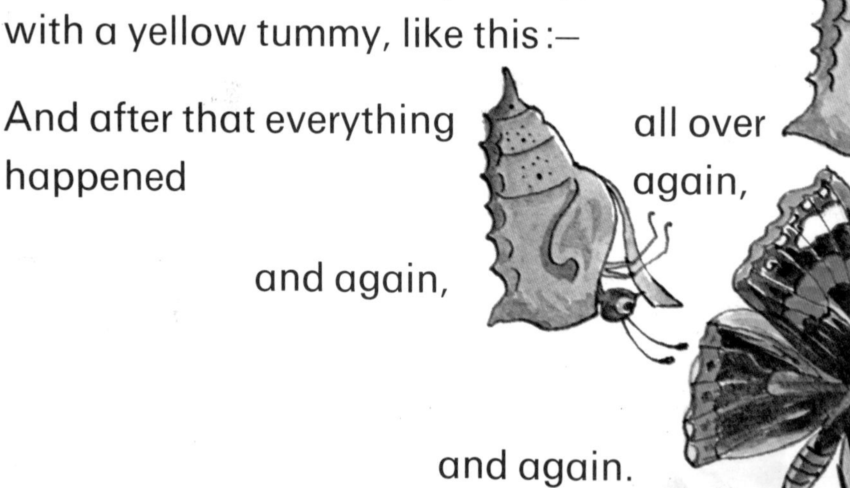

And after that everything happened all over again,

and again,

and again.